The Divatastic Be's

A GIRL'S GUIDEBOOK TO STEM CAREERS

Written by
Nancy Franklin-Wright

Believe It, Dream It, Achieve It!

~ Nancy Franklin-Wright

Divatastic Be's

A Girl's Guidebook to STEM Careers

ISBN: 978-1-7363609-3-4 (Paperback)
ISBN: 978-1-7363609-1-0 (eBook)
ISBN: 978-1-7363609-5-8 (Hardback)

Library of Congress Cataloging -in Publication data is on file with the publisher.

Visit www.authornfranklinwright.com

The Divatastic Be's

A GIRL'S GUIDEBOOK TO STEM CAREERS

Written by Nancy Franklin-Wright

Divatastic Be's want to be lots of things when they grow up, you see.

I work with NASA as an Astronaut. I take a trip to outer space, taking a closer look at the galaxy and watching the other planets in orbit.
What a sight to see.

How much fun it would be, eating lunch upside down.
Yippee!

I play with dolphins and study whales. I am a **Marine Biologist** out in the great big blue sea. Showing care and concern for water creatures really makes my day.

Every time I'm around them, I never want to leave,
and always want to stay.
Splish, Splash, just like taking a bath.

Come along and watch me ride around a racetrack in the car that I helped build and design.

Working as an Auto Aerodynamic Designer is so much fun.

I help build big cars, little cars, red cars, silvers cars and even flying cars. Look at it go.... up.... down, all around, without even making a sound.

Before the end of the day, a friend and I get together to play video games.

As a Software Developer, I test the systems I create, making sure that they work properly and that there are no mistakes.

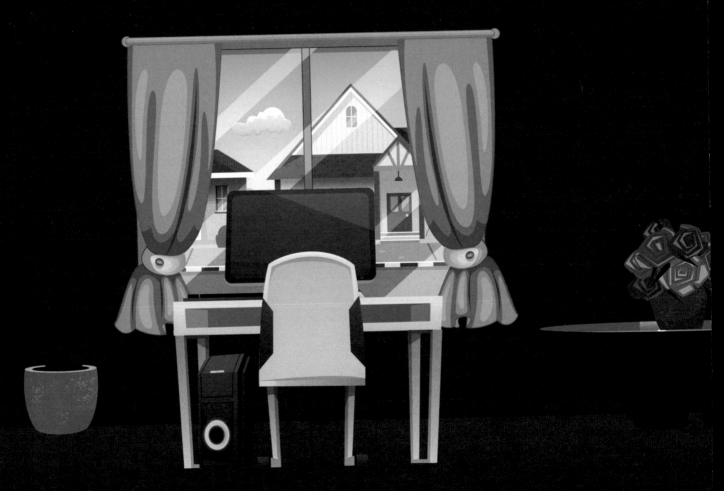

What a bummer it would be if we started playing our video game and it would cut off suddenly.
Oh no!

Just imagine how fun it would be to take a ride with me!

I am a Civil Engineer who designed and helped build the newest, fastest, safest roller coaster for our amusement park.

It has glowing lights that can be seen in the dark.

An awesome day of adventure on the roller coaster,
with the first ride being free.
Laughs and giggles are all we'll hear,
as we make it a great time - one of the best this year!

Neighborhood pets come to visit when they have a belly ache that needs to be relieved.

I'm a Vet. You bet!

I just love to help them feel better.
And afterward, I give them a great big hug.

Oh, how exciting it is to be a Divatastic Be!
We like to watch movies and eat popcorn with our family.

Summertime fun is the best with friends we meet, when we take swimming pool dips and stop for ice cream treats.
Never wanting the day to end, we'll wake up in the morning to do it again.

Be yourself, do your best, be all that you can be!
And you'll see how easy it is to be

Divatastically Me!

Nancy Franklin-Wright is a talented children's book author, who's reputable for her great passion for empowering young girls with great value to grow into confident, responsible, and focused adults. Nancy has a vast wealth or experience working with children as a volunteer and in a paid position. She is the founder of the D.I.V.A's (Daring, Inspired, Victorious, Awesome) Club, which focuses on helping girls of ages 6-12 to develop leadership skills, enhance their self-esteem, and other positive character traits.

Nancy's competency while working with children lies in her great sense of focus and the array of highly engaging, versatile, and effective methods that she uses to coach them. She holds a Bachelor's degree in Healthcare Administration, a Master's (with honors) in Human Resource Management and has taken an undergraduate course in Introduction to Education.

In her spare time, Nancy enjoys spending quality time with her family and friends, baking, eating good food, reading, exercising, photography, and singing.

Made in United States
Orlando, FL
07 September 2022